SONGS YOU *Think* YOU KNOW

compiled by
Donald Maxwell-Timmins

Schofield & Sims Limited Huddersfield

0 7217 2537 6

0 7217 2538 4 Net Edition

First printed 1986

Design and Artwork by Armitage Typo/Graphics Ltd., Huddersfield
Printed in England by Martin's of Berwick

Preface

How often have you been watching television, listening to the radio, been at a concert, taking part in a singsong or heard the familiar music to a song, thought you knew the words, then found that you couldn't get past the first line or so? It happens only too often to most people. This collection of 104 "well-known" songs will enable you to join in fully, so that next time . . .

As the melodies to these songs are usually so well known, the book can, of course, be used as a general song book for any occasion: at home, at clubs, on coach trips, at private parties and in school.

Opportunities for singing together are often missed these days, and this form of music-making is the least expensive, the oldest and possibly the most enjoyable.

So this time . . . join in the chorus!

Donald Maxwell-Timmins

Acknowledgements

The compiler and the publishers wish to thank the following for permission to use copyright material:

Southern Music Publishing Co. Ltd., 8 Denmark Street, London WC2H 8LT, for *Clementine* and *You Are My Sunshine*.

Bosworth & Co. Ltd., for *The Happy Wanderer*. ©copyright 1954 Bosworth & Co. Ltd., London.

Redwood Music Ltd., for *If You Were The Only Girl In The World*. Used by permission of Redwood Music Ltd., 14 New Burlington Street, London W1X 2LR.

Music Sales Ltd., for *Macnamara's Band*. Words: John J. Stamford. Copyright ©1917 Edwin Ashdown Limited, 78 Newman Street, London W1P 3LA. All rights reserved.

Campbell Connelly & Co. Ltd., for *Show Me The Way To Go Home* by Irving King. Copyright ©1925 by Campbell Connelly & Co. Ltd., 78 Newman Street, London W1P 3LA. All rights reserved. Also for, *Underneath The Arches* by Bud Flanagan. Copyright ©1932 by Campbell Connelly & Co. Ltd. All rights reserved.

CBS Songs, 3-5 Rathbone Place, London W1P 1DA, for *Side By Side, There's Something About A Soldier, We'll Keep A Welcome, When I'm Sixty Four, Yellow Submarine* and *Yesterday*.

EMI Music Publishing Ltd. and International Music Publications, for:
A Nightingale Sang in Berkeley Square by Eric Maschwitz. ©1940 Peter Maurice Music Co. Ltd., London WC2H 0LD.
Any Old Iron by Charles Collins, E. A. Shepherd and Fred Terry. ©1911 Herman Darewski Music Publishing Co., London WC2H 0LD.
Auf Wiederseh'n Sweetheart by John Sexton and John Turner. ©1952 Edition Corso GmbH, Germany. Sub-published by Peter Maurice Music Co. Ltd., London WC2H 0LD.
Bless 'Em All by Jimmy Hughes and Frank Lake. ©1940 Keith Prowse Music Publishing Co. Ltd., London WC2H 0LD.
By The Side Of The Zuyder Zee by A. J. Mills. ©1906 B. Feldman & Co. Ltd., London WC2H 0LD.
Congratulations by Bill Martin and Phil Coulter. ©1968 Peter Maurice Music Co. Ltd., London WC2H 0LD.
Down At The Old Bull And Bush by Andrew B. Sterling, Russell Hunting and Percy Krone. ©1903 Harry Von Tilzer Music Publishing Co., U.S.A. Sub-published by B. Feldman & Co. Ltd., London WC2H 0LD.
Fall In And Follow Me by A. J. Mills. ©1910 B. Feldman & Co. Ltd., London WC2H 0LD.
Fings Aint Wot They Used To Be by Lionel Bart. ©1960 Peter Maurice Music Co. Ltd., London WC2H 0LD.
Hello, Hello, Who's Your Lady Friend? by Worton David and Bert Lee. ©1913 B. Feldman & Co. Ltd., London WC2H 0LD.
Honeysuckle And The Bee by A. H. Fitz. ©1901 Sol Bloom, U.S.A. Sub-published by Francis Day & Hunter Ltd., London WC2H 0LD.
I'm Twenty-One Today by Alec Kendal. ©1911 B. Feldman & Co. Ltd., London WC2H 0LD.
In The Shade Of The Old Apple Tree by Harry Williams. ©1905 Remick Music Corp., U.S.A. Sub-published by Francis Day & Hunter Ltd., London WC2H 0LD.
It's A Long Way To Tipperary by Jack Judge and Harry Williams. ©1912 B. Feldman & Co. Ltd., London WC2H 0LD.
I Wonder Who's Kissing Her Now? by Will Hough and Frank Adams. ©1909 C. K. Harris Publishing Co. Inc., U.S.A. Sub-published by B. Feldman & Co. Ltd., London WC2H 0LD.

Abide With Me

Abide with me, fast falls the eventide;
The darkness deepens, Lord, with me abide;
When other helpers fail and comforts flee,
Help of the helpless, O abide with me.

Swift to its close ebbs out life's little day;
Earth's joys grow dim, its glories pass away;
Change and decay in all around I see—
O Thou Who changest not, abide with me.

I need Thy presence every passing hour;
What but Thy grace can foil the tempter's power?
Who like Thyself my guide and stay can be?
Through cloud and sunshine, O abide with me.

I fear no foe, with Thee at hand to bless;
Ills have no weight, and tears no bitterness.
Where is death's sting? Where, grave, thy victory?
I triumph still, if Thou abide with me.

Reveal Thyself before my closing eyes,
Shine through the gloom, and point me to the skies;
Heaven's morning breaks, and earth's vain shadows flee—
In life, in death, O Lord, abide with me.

All The Nice Girls

All the nice girls love a sailor,
All the nice girls love a tar;
For there's something about a sailor,
Well, you know what sailors are.
Bright and breezy, free and easy,
He's the ladies' pride and joy;
Falls in love with Kate and Jane,
Then he's off to sea again,
Ship ahoy, ship ahoy.

Alouette

Chorus Alouette, gentille Alouette,
Alouette, je te plumerai.

Je te plumerai la tête, je te plumerai la tête,
Ah, la tête, ah, la tête, Alouette, Alouette,
Alouette, gentille Alouette,
Alouette, je te plumerai.

Je te plumerai le bec, . . .

Je te plumerai le dos, . . .

Je te plumerai les pattes, . . .

Je te plumerai la "falle", . . .

Je te plumerai la queue, . . .

Amazing Grace

Amazing grace! how sweet the sound
That saved a wretch like me;
I once was lost, but now am found;
Was blind, but now I see.

'Twas grace that taught my heart to fear,
And grace my fears relieved;
How precious did that grace appear,
The hour I first believed!

Through many dangers, toils and snares
I have already come:
'Tis grace that brought me safe thus far,
And grace will lead me home.

The Lord has promised good to me,
His word my hope secures;
He will my shield and portion be
As long as life endures.

Yes, when this heart and flesh shall fail,
And mortal life shall cease,
I shall possess within the veil
A life of joy and peace.

When we've been there a thousand years,
Bright shining as the sun,
We've no less days to sing God's praise
Than when we first begun.

A Nightingale Sang
In Berkeley Square

That certain night, the night we met,
There was magic abroad in the air,
There were angels dining at the Ritz,
And a nightingale sang in Berkeley Square.
I may be right, I may be wrong,
But I'm perfectly willing to swear
That when you turned and smiled at me
A nightingale sang in Berkeley Square.
The moon that lingered over London Town,
Poor puzzled moon, he wore a frown;
How could he know we two were so in love,
The whole darned world seemed upside down?
The streets of town were paved with stars,
It was such a romantic affair,
And as we kissed and said goodnight
A nightingale sang in Berkeley Square.

Annie Laurie

Maxwellton braes are bonnie, where early falls the dew,
And 'twas there that Annie Laurie gave me her promise
true;
Gave me her promise true, which ne'er forgot will be,
And for bonny Annie Laurie I'd lay me down and dee.

Her brow is like the snowdrift, her neck is like the swan;
Her face it is the fairest that e'er the sun shone on;
That e'er the sun shone on, and dark blue is her e'e,
And for bonny Annie Laurie I'd lay me down and dee.

Like dew on the gowan lying is the fall of her fairy feet,
And like winds in summer sighing, her voice is low and
sweet;
Her voice is low and sweet, and she's all the world to me,
And for bonnie Annie Laurie I'd lay me down and dee.

Any Old Iron

Any old iron, any old iron,
Any, any, any old iron?
You look neat, talk about a treat,
You look dapper from your napper to your feet.
Dressed in style, brand new tile,
And your father's old green tie on,
But I wouldn't give you tuppence for your old watch chain,
Old iron, old iron?

Auf Wiederseh'n Sweetheart

Auf Wiederseh'n, auf Wiederseh'n,
We'll meet again sweetheart.
This lovely day has flown away,
The time has come to part.
We'll kiss again like this again,
Don't let the tear drops start,
With love that's true I'll wait for you,
Auf Wiederseh'n sweetheart.

Auld Lang Syne

Should auld acquaintance be forgot,
And never brought to mind?
Should auld acquaintance be forgot,
And days of auld lang syne?

Chorus For auld lang syne, my dear,
For auld lang syne;
We'll take a cup of kindness yet,
For auld lang syne.

And here's a hand, my trusty friend,
And gie's a hand o' thine;
We'll take a cup of kindness yet,
For auld lang syne.

Battle Hymn Of The Republic

Mine eyes have seen the glory of the coming of the Lord,
He is trampling out the vintage where the grapes of wrath
are stored;
He hath loosed the fateful lightning of his terrible swift sword:
His truth is marching on.

Chorus Glory, glory, hallelujah,
Glory, glory, hallelujah,
Glory, glory, hallelujah,
His truth is marching on.

In the beauty of the lilies Christ was born across the sea,
With a glory in his bosom that transfigures you and me;
As he died to make men holy, let us live to make men free,
His truth is marching on.

Blaydon Races

I went to Blaydon Races, 'twas on the ninth of June,
Eighteen hundred and sixty two on a summer's afternoon,
I took the bus from Balmbra's, and she was heavy laden,
Away we went along Collingwood Street that's on the road to
                                                                    Blaydon.

Chorus Oh lads, you should have seen us gannin',
            Passing the folks upon the road
            Just as they were standin'.
            There were lots of lads and lasses there
            All with smiling faces,
            Gannin' along the Scotswood Road
            To see the Blaydon Races.

We flew past Armstrong's factory and up to the Robin Adair,
Just gannin' down the railway bridge the bus wheel flew off there;
The lasses lost their crinolines and the veils that hide their faces,
I got two black eyes and a broken nose in gannin' to
                                                                    Blaydon Races.

When we got the wheel put on away we went again,
But them that had their noses broke they came back ower hyem;
Some went to the dispensary and some to Doctor Gibbs,
And some to the Infirmary to mend their broken ribs.

We flew across the Tyne Bridge right into Blaydon Town,
The bellman he was calling there, they called him Jacky Brown,
I saw him talking to some chaps and them he was persuading
To gan and see Geordie Ridley's show at the Mechanics Hall in
                                                                    Blaydon.

Bless 'Em All

Bless 'em all, bless 'em all,
The long and the short and the tall;
Bless all the sergeants and double-u-o ones,
Bless all the corporals and their blinking sons,
'Cos we're saying goodbye to them all
As back to their billets they crawl;
You'll get no promotion this side of the ocean
So cheer up, my lads, bless 'em all.

They say there's a troopship just leaving Bombay
Bound for old Blighty shore,
Heavily laden with time-expired men,
Bound for the land they adore.
There's many a soldier just finishing his time,
There's many a twerp signing on;
You'll get no promotion this side of the ocean,
So cheer up, my lads, bless 'em all.

Bless 'em all, bless 'em all,
The long and the short and the tall;
Bless all the sergeants and double-u-o ones,
Bless all the corporals and their blinking sons,
'Cos we're saying goodbye to them all
As back to their billets they crawl;
You'll get no promotion this side of the ocean
So cheer up, my lads, bless 'em all.

Bridge Over Troubled Waters

When you're weary, feeling small,
When tears are in your eyes,
I'll dry them all, I'm on your side.
Oh when times get rough,
And friends just can't be found,
Like a bridge over troubled waters
I will lay me down,
Like a bridge over troubled waters,
I will lay me down.

By The Side Of The Zuyder Zee

By the side of the Zuyder Zee,
Zuyder Zee, Zuyder Zee,
There my Deitcher girl waits for me, only me,
I've seen diamonds in Amsterdam,
Amsterdam, Amsterdam,
But there's not a diamond as bright as those eyes
By the Zuyder Zee.

Clementine

In a cavern, in a canyon, excavating for a mine,
Dwelt a miner, forty-niner, and his daughter, Clementine.

Chorus Oh my darling, oh my darling,
Oh my darling Clementine,
You are lost and gone for ever,
Dreadful sorry, Clementine.

Light she was as any fairy, and her shoes were number nine,
Herring boxes without topses, sandals were for Clementine.

Drove she ducklings to the water one fine morning just at nine,
Hit her foot against a splinter, fell in to the foaming brine.

Rosy lips above the water blowing bubbles mighty fine,
But alas! I was no swimmer, so I lost my Clementine.

Then the miner, forty-niner, soon began to peak and pine,
Thought he ought to join his daughter, now he's with his
Clementine.

In the churchyard, near the river, there a myrtle doth entwine,
With some roses and other posies, springing straight from
Clementine.

In my dreams she still doth haunt me, robed in garlands soaked
in brine,
Though in life I used to hug her, now she's dead, I draw the line.

How I missed her, how I missed her, how I missed my
Clementine,
But I kissed her little sister, and forgot my Clementine.

Climb Every Mountain

Climb ev'ry mountain, search high and low,
Follow ev'ry byway, ev'ry path you know.
Climb ev'ry mountain, ford ev'ry stream,
Follow ev'ry rainbow, till you find your dream.

A dream that will need all the love you can give,
Ev'ry day of your life for as long as you live.

Climb ev'ry mountain, ford ev'ry stream,
Follow ev'ry rainbow, till you find your dream.

Cockles And Mussels

In Dublin's fair city, where the girls are so pretty,
I first set my eyes on sweet Molly Malone,
As she wheeled her wheelbarrow through streets broad
and narrow,
Crying "Cockles and mussels alive, alive oh!"

Chorus Alive, alive oh! Alive, alive oh!
Crying "Cockles and mussels, alive, alive oh!"

She was a fishmonger, but sure 'twas no wonder,
For so were her father and mother before;
And they each wheeled their barrow through streets broad
and narrow,
Crying "Cockles and mussels, alive, alive oh!".

She died of a fever, and no one could save her,
And that was the end of sweet Molly Malone;
Her ghost wheels her barrow through streets broad and
narrow,
Crying "Cockles and mussels, alive, alive oh!".

Come Landlord, Fill The Flowing Bowl

Come landlord, fill the flowing bowl, until it doth run over,
Come landlord, fill the flowing bowl, until it doth run over,
For tonight we'll merry merry be, for tonight we'll merry be,
For tonight we'll merry merry be, tomorrow we'll be sober,
For tonight we'll merry be, for tonight we'll merry be
For tonight we'll merry be, tomorrow we'll be sober.

The man that drinketh small beer, and goes to bed quite sober,
Fades as the leaves do fade, fades as the leaves do fade,
Fades as the leaves do fade, that drop off in October,
Fades as the leaves do fade, fades as the leaves do fade,
Fades as the leaves do fade, that drop off in October.

The man who drinketh strong beer, and goes to bed right
mellow,
Lives as he ought to live, lives as he ought to live,
Lives as he ought to live, and dies a jolly good fellow,
Lives as he ought to live, lives as he ought to live,
Lives as he ought to live, and dies a jolly good fellow.

But he who drinks just what he likes, and getteth half-seas over,
Will live until he die perhaps, will live until he die perhaps,
Will live until he die perhaps, and then lie down in clover,
Will live until he die perhaps, will live until he die perhaps,
Will live until he die perhaps, and then lie down in clover.

The man who kisses a pretty girl, and goes and tells his
mother,
Ought to have his lips cut off, ought to have his lips cut off,
Ought to have his lips cut off, and never kiss another,
Ought to have his lips cut off, ought to have his lips cut off,
Ought to have his lips cut off, and never kiss another.

Congratulations

Congratulations and celebrations,
When I tell ev'ryone that you're in love with me.
Congratulations and jubilations,
I want the world to know I'm happy as can be.

Who would believe that I could be happy and contented,
I used to think that happiness hadn't been invented,
But that was in the bad old days before I met you,
When I let you walk into my heart.

Congratulations and celebrations,
When I tell ev'ryone that you're in love with me.
Congratulations and jubilations,
I want the world to know I'm happy as can be.

Daisy Bell

Daisy, Daisy, give me your answer do;
I'm half crazy, all for the love of you!
It won't be a stylish marriage,
We can't afford a carriage,
But you'll look sweet, upon the seat
Of a bicycle made for two.

Danny Boy

Oh, Danny boy, the pipes, the pipes are calling
From glen to glen, and down the mountain side;
The summer's gone, and all the roses fading,
Tis you, tis you must go and I must bide.
But come ye back when summer's in the meadow
Or when the valley's hushed and white with snow,
For I'll be here, in sunshine or in shadow,
O Danny boy, O Danny boy I love you so.

Don't Dilly Dally On The Way

My old man said "Follow the van,
And don't dilly-dally on the way."
Off went the van with me old man in it,
I followed on with me old cock linnet,
But I dillied and dallied, dallied and dillied,
Lost me way and don't know where to roam;
You can't trust a special like the old-time coppers,
And I can't find my way home.

Down At The Old Bull And Bush

Come, come, come and make eyes at me
Down at the old Bull and Bush;
Come, come, drink some port wine with me
Down at the old Bull and Bush.
Hear the little German Band,
Just let me hold your hand, dear.
Do, do, come and have a drink with me
Down at the old Bull and Bush.

Drink To Me Only

Drink to me only with thine eyes,
And I will pledge with mine;
Or leave a kiss within the cup,
And I'll not ask for wine;
The thirst that from the soul doth rise
Doth ask a drink divine,
But might I of love's nectar sip,
I would not change for thine.

I sent thee late a rosy wreath,
Not so much honouring thee,
As giving it a hope that there
It could not withered be.
But thou thereon didst only breathe,
And sent'st it back to me,
Since when it grows, and smells, I swear,
Not of itself but thee.

Edelweiss

Edelweiss, edelweiss, ev'ry morning you greet me,
Small and white, clean and bright,
You look happy to meet me.
Blossom of snow, may you bloom and grow,
Bloom and grow for ever,
Edelweiss, edelweiss, bless my homeland for ever.

Fall In And Follow Me

Fall in and follow me,
Fall in and follow me.
Come along and never mind the weather,
All together, stand on me boys,
I know the way to go,
I'll take you for a spree,
You do as I do and you'll do right,
Fall in and follow me.

Fings Ain't Wot They Used To Be

They've changed our local palais into a
                                    bowling alley,
And fings ain't wot they used to be.
There's Teds with drainpipe trousers
                    and debs in coffee houses,
And fings ain't wot they used to be.
It used to be fun, Dad and old Mum,
Paddling down Southend,
But now it ain't done, never mind chum,
Paris is where we spend our outings.
Grandma tries to shock us all,
Doing knees up rock and roll,
Fings ain't wot they used to be.

God Bless The Prince Of Wales

Among our ancient mountains and from our
lovely vales,
Oh, let the prayer re-echo, "God bless the
Prince of Wales."
With heart and voice awaken those minstrel
strains of yore,
Till Britain's name and glory resound from
shore to shore.

Chorus Among our ancient mountains and
from our lovely vales,
Oh, let the prayer re-echo, "God bless
the Prince of Wales."

Should hostile bands or danger e'er threaten
our fair Isle,
May God's strong arm protect us, may Heaven
still on us smile;
Above the throne of England may fortune's
star long shine,
And round its sacred bulwarks the olive
branches twine.

God Save The Queen

God save our gracious Queen,
Long live our noble Queen,
God save the Queen!
Send her victorious,
Happy and glorious,
Long to reign over us,
God save the Queen.

Thy choicest gifts in store,
On her be pleased to pour,
Long may she reign.
May she defend our laws,
And ever give us cause
To sing, with heart and voice,
God save the Queen.

Goodnight Ladies

Goodnight, ladies! Goodnight ladies!
Goodnight ladies! We're going to leave you now.

Chorus Merrily we roll along, roll along, roll along,
Merrily we roll along, o'er the deep blue sea.

Farewell, ladies! Farewell ladies!
Farewell, ladies! You're going to leave us now.

Sweet dreams, ladies! Sweet dreams, ladies!
Sweet dreams, ladies! We're going to leave you now.

Hello, Hello, Who's Your Lady Friend?

Hello, hello, who's your lady friend?
Who's the little girlie by your side?
I've seen you with a girl or two,
Oh, oh, oh, I am surprised at you.
Hello, hello, stop your little games,
Don't you think your ways you ought to mend?
It isn't the girl I saw you with at Brighton;
Who, who, who's your lady friend?

Home On The Range

Oh, give me a home where the buffalo roam,
Where the deer and the antelope play.
Where never is heard a discouraging word,
And the skies are not cloudy or grey.

Chorus Home, home on the range,
Where the deer and the antelope play;
Where never is heard a discouraging word,
And the skies are not cloudy or grey.

Where often at night when the heavens were bright
With the light of the glittering stars,
I have stood there amazed and asked as I gazed,
Does their glory exceed that of ours?

Home Sweet Home

'Mid pleasures and palaces though we may roam,
Be it ever so humble, there's no place like home!
A charm from the skies seems to hallow us there,
Which, seen through the world, is ne'er met with elsewhere.

Chorus Home! Home! Sweet, sweet, home!
There's no place like home,
There's no place like home!

An exile from home, splendour dazzles in vain;
Oh, give me my lowly thatched cottage again!
The birds singing gaily, that came at my call,
Give me them, and that peace of mind dearer than all.

Honeysuckle And The Bee

You are my honey, honeysuckle, I am the bee;
I'd like to sip the honey sweet from those red lips you see.
I love you dearly, dearly, and I want you to love me;
You are my honey, honeysuckle, I am the bee.

I Do Like To Be Beside The Seaside

Oh, I do like to be beside the seaside,
I do like to be beside the sea;
I do like to stroll upon the Prom, Prom, Prom,
Where the brass bands play "Tiddely-om-pom-pom".
So just let me be beside the seaside,
I'll be beside myself with glee,
And there's lots of girls beside,
I should like to be beside,
Beside the seaside, beside the sea.

If You Were The Only Girl In The World

If you were the only girl in the world,
And I were the only boy,
Nothing else would matter in the world today,
We could go on loving in the same old way.
A garden of Eden, just made for two,
With nothing to mar our joy;
I would say such wonderful things to you,
There would be such wonderful things to do,
If you were the only girl in the world,
And I were the only boy.

I'll Be Your Sweetheart

I'll be your sweetheart if you will be mine.
All my life I'll be your Valentine.
Bluebells I've gathered, keep them and be true.
When I'm a man my plan will be to marry you.

I'm Twenty-One Today

I'm twenty-one today, twenty-one today;
I've got the key of the door,
Never been twenty-one before;
And pa says I can do as I like;
So shout, "Hip, hip, hooray.
He's a jolly good fellow, twenty-one today."

In The Shade Of The Old Apple Tree

In the shade of the old apple tree,
When the love in your eyes I could see,
When the voice that I heard, like the song of a bird,
Seemed to whisper sweet music to me.
I could hear the dull buzz of a bee
In the garden, when you said to me:
"With a heart that is true, I'll be waiting for you
In the shade of the old apple tree."

It's A Long Way To Tipperary

It's a long way to Tipperary,
It's a long way to go;
It's a long way to Tipperary,
To the sweetest girl I know.
Goodbye, Piccadilly,
Farewell, Leicester Square,
It's a long, long way to Tipperary,
But my heart's right there.

I Wonder Who's Kissing Her Now?

I wonder who's kissing her now?
Wonder who's teaching her now?
Wonder who's looking into her eyes,
Breathing sighs, telling lies?
I wonder if she's got a boy,
The girl who once filled me with joy?
Wonder if she ever tells him of me?
I wonder who's kissing her now?

Jerusalem

And did those feet in ancient time
Walk upon England's mountains green?
And was the holy Lamb of God
On England's pleasant pastures seen?
And did the countenance divine
Shine forth upon our clouded hills?
And was Jerusalem builded here,
Among those dark, satanic mills?

Bring me my bow of burning gold!
Bring me my arrows of desire!
Bring me my spear! O clouds unfold!
Bring me my chariot of fire!
I will not cease from mental fight,
Nor shall my sword sleep in my hand
Till we have built Jerusalem
In England's green and pleasant land.

Jeanie With The Light Brown Hair

I dream of Jeanie with the light brown hair
Borne, like a zephyr, on the summer air;
I see her tripping where the bright streams play;
Happy are the daisies that dance on her way.
Many were the wild notes her merry voice would pour,
Many were the blithe birds that warbled them o'er.
I dream of Jeanie with the light brown hair,
Floating, like a zephyr, on the soft summer air.

I long for Jeanie with the gay dawn smile,
Radiant in gladness, warm with winning guile;
I hear her melodies, like joys gone by,
Sighing round my heart o'er the fond hopes that die;
Sighing like the night wind and sobbing like the rain,
Waiting for the lost one that comes not again.
I sigh for Jeanie with the light brown hair,
Floating like a zephyr, on the soft summer air.

Jingle Bells

Dashing through the snow in a one-horse open sleigh;
O'er the fields we go, laughing all the way.
Bells on bobtail ring, making spirits bright;
What fun it is to ride and sing a sleighing song tonight!

Chorus Jingle bells, jingle bells, jingle all the way.
Oh what fun it is to ride in a one-horse open sleigh.
Jingle bells, jingle bells, jingle all the way.
Oh what fun it is to ride in a one-horse open sleigh.

A day or two ago I thought I'd take a ride,
And soon Miss Fannie Bright was seated by my side.
The horse was lean and lank, misfortune seemed his lot,
He got into a drifted bank, and we, we got upsot.

Now the ground is white go it while you're young,
Take the girls tonight, and sing this sleighing song;
Just get a bobtailed nag, two-forty for his speed,
Then hitch him to an open sleigh and, crack, you'll take
the lead.

John Brown's Body

John Brown's body lies a-mould'ring in the grave,
John Brown's body lies a-mould'ring in the grave,
John Brown's body lies a-mould'ring in the grave,
But his soul goes marching on.

Chorus Glory, glory, hallelujah!
Glory, glory, hallelujah!
Glory, glory, hallelujah!
His soul goes marching on.

John Brown died that the slave might be free,
John Brown died that the slave might be free,
John Brown died that the slave might be free,
But his soul goes marching on.

Now has come the glorious jubilee,
Now has come the glorious jubilee,
Now has come the glorious jubilee,
But his soul goes marching on.

Knees Up Mother Brown

Knees up Mother Brown,
Knees up Mother Brown,
Come along dearie let it go,
Ee-i-ee-i-ee-i-oh.
It's your blooming birthday,
Let's wake up all the town.
So, knees up, knees up,
Don't get the breeze up,
Knees up Mother Brown.

Land Of Hope And Glory

Land of hope and glory, mother of the free,
How shall we extol thee, who are born of thee?
Wider still and wider shall thy bounds be set;
God, who made thee mighty, make thee mightier yet,
God, who made thee mighty, make thee mightier yet.

Land Of My Fathers

Oh, land of my fathers, the land of the free,
The home of the harp so soothing to me,
Thy noble defenders were gallant and brave,
For freedom their heart's life they gave.

Chorus Wales, Wales, home sweet home is Wales.
Till death be passed my love shall last,
My longing, my yearning for Wales.

Thou Eden of bards, and birthplace of song,
The sons of thy mountains are valiant and strong;
The voice of thy streamlets is soft to the ear,
Thy hills and thy valleys so dear.

Though slighted and scorned by the proud and the strong,
The language of Cambria still charms us in song;
The genius survives, nor have envious tales
Yet silenced the harp of dear Wales.

Lilli Marlene

Underneath the lantern, by the barrack gate,
Darling, I remember the way you used to wait;
'Twas there that you whispered tenderly
That you loved me, you'd always be
My Lilli of the lamplight, my own Lilli Marlene.

Time would come for roll call, time for us to part,
Darling I'd caress you and press you to my heart;
And there, 'neath that far off lantern light,
I'd hold you tight, we'd kiss goodnight,
My Lilli of the lamplight, my own Lilli Marlene.

Orders came for sailing, somewhere over there,
All confined to barracks was more than I could bear;
I knew you were waiting in the street,
I heard your feet, but could not meet
My Lilli of the lamplight, my own Lilli Marlene.

Resting in a billet, just behind the line,
Even though we're parted your lips are close to mine;
You wait where that lantern softly gleams,
Your sweet face seems to haunt my dreams,
My Lilli of the lamplight, my own Lilli Marlene.

Little Brown Jug

My wife and I lived all alone,
In a little log hut we called our own;
She loved gin and I loved rum,
I tell you what – we'd lots of fun.

Chorus Ha-ha-ha, you and me,
Little brown jug, don't I love thee!
Ha-ha-ha, you and me,
Little brown jug, don't I love thee!

'Tis you who make my friends my foes,
'Tis you who make me wear old clothes;
Here you are so near my nose,
So tip her up and down she goes.

If I'd a cow that gave such milk,
I'd clothe her in the finest silk;
I'd feed her on the choicest hay,
And milk her forty times a day.

The rose is red, my nose is too,
The violet's blue, and so are you;
And yet I guess, before I stop,
I'd better take another drop.

Loch Lomond

By yon bonnie banks and by yon bonnie braes,
Where the sun shines bright on Loch Lomond,
Where me and my true love were ever wont to gae,
On the bonnie, bonnie banks of Loch Lomond.

Chorus Oh, ye'll take the high road, and I'll take the low
road,
And I'll be in Scotland afore ye,
But me and my true love will never meet again,
On the bonnie, bonnie banks of Loch Lomond.

'Twas there that we parted in yon shady glen,
On the steep, steep side of Ben Lomond,
Where in purple hue the Highland hills we view,
And the moon coming out in the gloamin'.

The wee birdies sing and the wild flowers spring,
And in sunshine the waters lie sleeping;
But the broken heart it kens nae second spring,
Though the waefu' may cease from their greeting.

Londonderry Air

In Derry vale, beside the singing river,
So oft I strayed, ah, many years ago,
And culled at morn the golden daffodillies
That came with Spring to set the word aglow.
O, Derry vale, my thoughts are ever turning
To your broad stream and fairy-circled lea,
For your green isles my exiled heart is yearning,
So far away across the sea.

In Derry vale, amid the Foyle's dark waters,
The salmon leap above the surging weir,
The sea-birds call – I still can hear them calling
In night's long streams of those so dear.
Oh, tarrying years, fly faster, ever faster,
I long to see the vale beloved so well,
I long to know that I am not forgotten,
And there at home in peace to dwell.

Macnamara's Band

My name is Macnamara, I'm the leader of the band,
And though we're small in number we're the best in all the land.
Oh, I am the conductor and we often have to play
With all the best musicianers you hear about today.
When the drums go bang, the cymbals clang, the horns will
blaze away,
McCarthy puffs the old bassoon while Doyle the pipes will play,
Oh, Hennessy Tennessy tootles the flute, my word 'tis
something grand,
Oh, a credit to old Ireland, boys, is Macnamara's band.
Tra la la la . . .

Whenever an election's on, we play on either side,
The way we play our fine old airs fills Irish hearts with pride.
If poor Tom Moore was living now he'd make you understand,
That none could do him justice like old Macnamara's band.
When the drums go bang, . . .

We play at wakes and weddings, and at ev'ry county ball,
And at any great man's funeral we play the "Dead March in
Saul".
When the Prince of Wales to Ireland came, he shook me by
the hand,
And said he'd never heard the like of Macnamara's band.
When the drums go bang, . . .

Madamoiselle From Armentières

Madamoiselle from Armentières, Parlez-vous?
Madamoiselle from Armentières, Same to you.
Who was the girl who lost her sheep
Through singing this chorus in her sleep?
Madamoiselle from Armentières.

Madamoiselle from Armentières, Parlez-vous?
Madamoiselle from Armentières, Same to you.
Who was it pinched the barber's pole,
And used it for fuel to save the coal?
Madamoiselle from Armentières.

Madamoiselle from Armentières, Parlez-vous?
Madamoiselle from Armentières, Same to you.
Who was it tied his kilt with string,
To stop it from doing the Highland fling?
Madamoiselle from Armentières.

Mary

For it is Mary, Mary, plain as any name can be,
But with propriety, society will say "Marie".
But it was Mary, Mary, long before the fashions came,
And there is something there that sounds so square,
It's a grand old name.

Maybe It's Because I'm A Londoner

Maybe it's because I'm a Londoner
That I love London so;
Maybe it's because I'm a Londoner
That I think of her wherever I go.
I get a funny feeling inside of me,
Just walking up and down;
Maybe it's because I'm a Londoner
That I love London town.

Men Of Harlech

Men of Harlech! In the hollow,
Do you hear the rushing billow,
Wave on wave that surging follow
Battle's distant sound?
'Tis the tramp of Saxon foemen,
Saxon spearmen, Saxon bowmen,
Be they knights, or hinds, or yeomen,
They shall bite the ground.
Loose the folds asunder,
Flag we conquer under!
The placid sky now bright on high
Shall launch its bolts in thunder!
Onward, 'tis our country needs us!
He is bravest, he who leads us!
Honour's self now proudly heads us!
Cambria, God, and right.

Michael, Row The Boat Ashore

Michael, row the boat ashore,
Hallelujah.
Michael, row the boat ashore,
Hallelujah.

Sister, help to trim the sail,
Hallelujah.
Sister, help to trim the sail,
Hallelujah.

Brother, won't you give a hand,
Hallelujah.
Brother, won't you give a hand,
Hallelujah.

Jordan's deep and Jordan's wide,
Hallelujah.
Jordan's deep and Jordan's wide,
Hallelujah.

My Bonnie

My Bonnie is over the ocean,
My Bonnie is over the sea,
My Bonnie is over the ocean,
O bring back my Bonnie to me.

Chorus Bring back, bring back,
 Bring back my bonnie to me, to me;
 Bring back, bring back,
 O bring back my Bonnie to me.

Last night as I lay on my pillow,
Last night as I lay on my bed,
Last night as I lay on my pillow,
I dreamed that my Bonnie was dead.

The winds have blown over the ocean,
The winds have blown over the sea,
The winds have blown over the ocean
And brought back my Bonnie to me.

My Grandfather's Clock

My Grandfather's clock was too large for the shelf,
So it stood ninety years on the floor;
It was taller by half than the old man himself,
Though it weighed not a penny-weight more.
It was bought on the morn of the day that he was born,
And was always his treasure and pride;
But it stopped short, never to go again
When the old man died.

Chorus Ninety years without slumbering,
      Tick, tock, tick, tock,
      His life seconds numbering,
      Tick, tock, tick, tock,
      It stopped short, never to go again
      When the old man died.

In watching its pendulum swing to and fro,
Many hours he spent while a boy;
And in childhood and manhood the clock seemed to know
And to share both his grief and his joy.
For it struck twenty-four when he entered at the door
With a blooming and beautiful bride;
But it stopped short, never to go again
When the old man died.

My grandfather said of those that he could hire,
Not a servant so faithful he found;
For it wasted no time and had but one desire
At the close of each week to be wound.
And it kept in its place, not a frown upon its face,
And its hands never hung by its side;
But it stopped short, never to go again
When the old man died.

My Old Dutch

I've got a pal, a reg'lar out and outer,
She's a dear old gal, I'll tell yer all about 'er,
It's many years since first we met,
'Er 'air was then as black as jet;
It's whiter now, but she don't fret,
Not my old gal.

We've been together now for forty years,
And it don't seem a day too much,
There ain't a lady livin' in the land
As I'd swap for my dear old Dutch,
There ain't a lady livin' in the land
As I'd swop for my dear old Dutch.

Nellie Dean

There's an old mill by the stream, Nellie Dean,
Where we used to sit and dream, Nellie Dean;
And the waters, as they flowed, seemed to murmur sweet
and low:
"You are my heart's desire; I love you, Nellie Dean."

Now Is The Hour

Now is the hour when we must say goodbye;
Soon you'll be sailing far across the sea.
While you're away, Oh please remember me,
When you return you'll find me waiting here.

Oh, Susanna

I come from Alabama with my banjo on my knee,
I'm going to Louisiana, my true love for to see.
It rained all night the day I left,
The weather it was dry,
The sun so hot I froze to death,
Susanna, don't you cry.

Chorus Oh, Susanna, O don't you cry for me;
I come from Alabama with my banjo on my knee.

I had a dream the other night when everything was still;
I thought I saw Susanna a-coming down the hill.
The buckwheat cake was in her mouth,
A tear was in her eye;
Says I, "I'm coming from the South,
Susanna, don't you cry."

O God Our Help

O God, our help in ages past,
Our hope for years to come,
Our shelter from the stormy blast,
And our eternal home;

Under the shadow of Thy throne
Thy saints have dwelt secure;
Sufficient is Thine arm alone,
And our defence is sure.

Before the hills in order stood,
Or earth received her frame,
From everlasting Thou art God,
To endless years the same.

A thousand ages in Thy sight
Are like an evening gone,
Short as the watch that ends the night
Before the rising sun.

Time, like an ever-rolling stream,
Bears all its sons away;
They fly forgotten, as a dream
Dies at the opening day.

O God, our help in ages past,
Our hope for years to come,
Be Thou our guard while troubles last,
And our eternal home.

On Ilkley Moor Baht 'at

Where hast thou been since I saw thee?
On Ilkley Moor baht 'at,
Where hast thou been since I saw thee?
Where hast thou been since I saw thee?
On Ilkley Moor baht 'at,
On Ilkley Moor baht 'at,
On Ilkley Moor baht 'at.

Thou's been a-courtin' Mary Jane . . .

Thou'll go and get thee death o' cold . . .

Then we shall have to bury thee . . .

Then t'worms'll come and eat thee up . . .

Then t'ducks'll come and eat up worms . . .

Then we shall go and eat up t'ducks . . .

Then we shall all have eaten thee . . .

That's where we gets us own back . . .

On Mother Kelly's Doorstep

On Mother Kelly's doorstep, down Paradise Row,
I'd sit along o' Nelly, she'd sit along o' Joe.
She'd got a little hole in her frock, hole in her shoe,
Hole in her sock where her toe peeped through,
But Nelly was the smartest down our alley.
On Mother Kelly's doorstep I'm wondering now
If little gal Nelly remembers Joe, her beau,
And does she love me like she used to,
On Mother Kelly's doorstep, down Paradise Row.

Pack Up Your Troubles

Hi! Pack up your troubles in your old kitbag,
And smile, smile, smile.
While you've a lucifer to light your fag,
Smile, boys, that's the style.
What's the use of worrying?
It never was worth while, so
Pack up your troubles in your old kitbag
And smile, smile, smile.

Polly Wolly Doodle

Oh I went down south for to see my Sal,
Sing Polly wolly doodle all the day;
My Sally am a spunky gal,
Sing Polly wolly doodle all the day.

Chorus Fare thee well, fare thee well,
Fare thee well, my fairy fay,
For I'm off to Louisiana for to see my Susyanna,
Sing Polly wolly doodle all the day.

Oh my Sal she am a maiden fair,
Sing polly wolly doodle all the day;
With curly eyes and laughing hair,
Sing Polly wolly doodle all the day.

A grasshopper sitting on a railroad track,
Sing Polly wolly doodle all the day;
A-picking his teeth with a carpet tack,
Sing Polly wolly doodle all the day.

Roll Out The Barrel

Roll out the barrel,
We'll have a barrel of fun.
Roll out the barrel,
We've got the blues on the run.
Zing! Boom! Ta-rarrel!
Ring out a song of good cheer.
Now's the time to roll the barrel,
For the gang's all here.

Rule, Britannia

When Britain first at Heaven's command
Arose from out the azure main,
Arose, arose, arose from out the azure main,
This was the charter, the charter of the land,
And guardian angels sang this strain:

Chorus Rule, Britannia, Britannia rules the waves,
Britons never never never, will be slaves.

The nations not so blest as thee,
Must in their turn to tyrants bend,
Must in their turn, must in their turn to tyrants bend.
While thou shalt flourish, shalt flourish great and free,
And to the weak protection lend.

The Muses, still with freedom found,
Shall to thy happy coast repair;
Shall to thy happy coast, thy happy coast repair,
Blest Isle! With beauty, with matchless beauty crown'd,
And manly hearts to guard the fair.

Sally

Sally, Sally, don't ever wander away from the alley and me,
Sally, Sally, marry me Sally, and happy for ever I'll be.
When skies are blue you're beguiling,
When they are grey you're still smiling, smiling,
Sally, Sally, pride of our alley,
You're more than the whole world to me.

She's A Lassie From Lancashire

She's a lassie from Lancashire,
Just a lassie from Lancashire.
She's a lassie that I love dear,
Oh, so dear.
Though she dresses in clogs and shawl,
She's the prettiest of them all.
None could be fairer or rarer than Sarah,
My lass from Lancashire.

She'll Be Coming Round The Mountains

She'll be coming round the mountains when she comes,
She'll be coming round the mountains when she comes,
She'll be coming round the mountains, coming round the
mountains,
She'll be coming round the mountains when she comes.

Chorus Singing i-yi-yippi-yippi-yay,
Singing i-yi-yippi-yippi-yay,
Singing i-yi-yippi, i-yi-yippi,
I-yi-yippi-yippi-yay.

She'll be wearing pink pyjamas when she comes,
She'll be wearing pink pyjamas when she comes,
She'll be wearing pink pyjamas, wearing pink pyjamas,
She'll be wearing pink pyjamas when she comes.

She'll be driving six white horses when she comes,
She'll be driving six white horses when she comes,
She'll be driving six white horses, driving six white horses,
She'll be driving six white horses when she comes.

Oh, we'll all go to meet her when she comes,
Oh, we'll all go to meet her when she comes,
Oh, we'll all go to meet her, all go to meet her,
Oh, we'll all go to meet her when she comes.

Show Me The Way To Go Home

Show me the way to go home,
I'm tired and I want to go to bed!
I had a little drink about an hour ago
And it's gone right to my head.
No matter where I roam,
On land or sea or foam,
You can always hear me singing this song,
Show me the way to go home.

Side By Side

Oh, we ain't got a barrel of money,
Maybe we're ragged and funny,
But we'll travel along, singing a song,
Side by side.
Don't know what's coming tomorrow,
Maybe it's trouble and sorrow,
But we'll travel the road, sharing our load,
Side by side.
Through all kinds of weather,
What if the sky should fall?
Just as long as we're together,
It doesn't matter at all.
When they've all had their quarrels and parted,
We'll be the same as we started,
Just travelling along, singing a song,
Side by side.

Sweet Genevieve

Oh, Genevieve, I'd give the world
To live again the lovely past!
The rose of youth was dew impearled,
But now it withers in the blast.
I see thy face in every dream,
My waking thoughts are full of thee;
Thy glance is in the starry beam
That falls along the summer sea.

Chorus Oh Genevieve, sweet Genevieve,
The days may come, the days may go,
But still the hands of mem'ry weave
The blissful dreams of long ago.

Fair Genevieve, my early love,
The years but make thee dearer far;
My heart shall never, never rove:
Thou art my only guiding star.
For me the past has no regret,
What e'er the years may bring to me;
I bless the hour when first we met,
The hour that gave me love and thee!

The Anniversary Waltz

Tell me I may always dance the Anniversary Waltz
                                                with you;
Tell me this is real romance, an anniversary dream
                                              come true.
Let this be the anthem to our future years,
To millions of smiles and a few little tears.
May I always listen to the Anniversary Waltz with you.

Take Me Back To Dear Old Blighty

Take me back to dear old Blighty,
Put me on the train for London Town,
Take me over there, drop me anywhere,
Liverpool, Leeds or Birmingham, well I don't care.
I should love to see my best girl
Cuddle-ing up again we soon should be,
So, tiddley-iddley-ighty, hurry me home to Blighty,
Blighty is the place for me.

The Chestnut Tree

Underneath the spreading chestnut tree
I loved her and she loved me,
There she used to sit upon my knee
'Neath the spreading chestnut tree.
There beneath the boughs we used to meet,
All her kisses were so sweet,
All the little birds went "tweet, tweet, tweet",
'Neath the spreading chestnut tree.
I said "I love you, and there ain't no ifs or buts".
She said "I love you" and the blacksmith shouted
                                    "Chestnuts"!
Underneath the spreading chestnut tree
There she said she'd marry me,
Now you ought to see our family,
'Neath the spreading chestnut tree.

57

The Drunken Sailor

What shall we do with a drunken sailor?
What shall we do with a drunken sailor?
What shall we do with a drunken sailor?
Early in the morning.

Chorus Hooray, and up she rises!
Hooray, and up she rises!
Hooray and up she rises,
Early in the morning!

Put him in the long boat till he's sober.
Put him in the long boat till he's sober.
Put him in the long boat till he's sober,
Early in the morning.

Give him a taste of the bosun's rope end.
Give him a taste of the bosun's rope end.
Give him a taste of the bosun's rope end,
Early in the morning.

Give him a dose of salt and water.
Give him a dose of salt and water.
Give him a dose of salt and water,
Early in the morning.

Put on his back a mustard plaster.
Put on his back a mustard plaster.
Put on his back a mustard plaster,
Early in the morning.

That's what to do with a drunken sailor.
That's what to do with a drunken sailor.
That's what to do with a drunken sailor,
Early in the morning.

The Happy Wanderer

I love to go a-wandering,
Along the mountain track,
And as I go, I love to sing,
My knapsack on my back.

Chorus Val-de ri, val-de ra,
Val-de ra, val-de ha ha ha
Ha ha ha, val-de ri,
Val-de ra,
My knapsack on my back.

Oh, may I go a-wandering
Until the day I die.
Oh, may I always laugh and sing,
Beneath God's clear blue sky.

The Isle Of Capri

'Twas on the Isle of Capri that I found her,
Beneath the shade of an old walnut tree,
Oh, I can still see the flowers blooming round her,
Where we met on the Isle of Capri.
She was as sweet as a rose at the dawning,
But somehow fate hadn't meant her for me,
And though I sailed with the tide in the morning,
Still my heart's on the Isle of Capri.
Summer time was nearly over,
Blue Italian sky above,
I said "Lady, I'm a rover,
Can you spare a sweet word of love?"
She whispered softly "It's best not to linger",
And then as I kissed her hand I could see
She wore a plain golden ring on her finger,
'Twas goodbye to the Isle of Capri.

The Lord's My Shepherd

The Lord's my Shepherd, I'll not want:
He makes me down to lie
In pastures green; He leadeth me
The quiet waters by.

My soul He doth restore again;
And me to walk doth make
Within the paths of righteousness,
E'en for His own name's sake.

Yea, though I walk through death's dark vale,
Yet will I fear none ill:
For Thou art with me; and Thy rod
And staff me comfort still.

My table thou hast furnishèd
In presence of my foes;
My head Thou dost with oil anoint,
And my cup overflows.

Goodness and mercy all my life
Shall surely follow me;
And in God's house for evermore
My dwelling-place shall be.

The Mountains O' Mourne

Oh Mary, this London's a wonderful sight,
With the people here working by day and by night;
They don't sow potatoes, nor barley, nor wheat,
But there's gangs of them digging for gold in the street.
At least, when I asked them, that's what I was told,
So I just took a hand at this digging for gold,
But for all that I found there I might as well be
Where the Mountains o' Mourne sweep down to the sea.

There's beautiful girls here, oh, never mind,
With beautiful shapes nature never designed,
And lovely complexions all roses and cream,
But O'Loughlin remarked with regard to the same:
That if at those roses you venture to sip
The colours might all come away on your lip,
So I'll wait for the wild rose that's waiting for me
Where the Mountains o' Mourne sweep down to the sea.

The Old Folks At Home

Way down upon the Swanee River,
Far, far away,
There's where my heart is turning ever,
There's where my old folks stay.
All up and down the whole creation
Sadly I roam,
Still longing for the old plantation
And for the old folks at home.

Chorus All the world is sad and dreary,
   Ev'rywhere I roam,
   Oh how my heart is turning weary,
   Far from the old folks at home.

All round the little farm I wandered,
When I was young;
Then many happy days I squandered,
Many the song I sung.
When I was playing with my brother,
Happy was I;
Oh! take me to my kind old mother,
There let me live and die.

The Quartermaster's Stores

There were rats, rats, big as bloomin' cats,
In the stores, in the stores.
There were rats, rats, lying about on mats,
In the Quartermaster's stores.

Chorus My eyes are dim, I cannot see,
      I have not brought my specs with me,
      I have not brought my specs with me.

There was steak, steak, tough as cattle cake,
In the stores, in the stores.
There was steak, steak, to give you belly ache,
In the Quartermaster's stores.

There was bread, bread, harder than your head,
In the stores, in the stores.
There was bread, bread, just like lumps of lead,
In the Quartermaster's stores.

The Red Flag

The people's flag is deepest red,
It shrouded oft our martyred dead,
And ere their limbs grew stiff and cold,
Their hearts' blood dyed its ev'ry fold.

Chorus Then raise the scarlet standard high!
Within its shade we'll live or die,
Though cowards flinch and traitors sneer,
We'll keep the red flag flying here.

It waved about our infant might,
When all ahead seemed dark as night;
It witnessed many a deed and vow;
We must not change its colour now.

It well recalls the triumphs past,
It gives the hope of peace at last;
The banner bright, the symbol plain,
Of human right and human gain.

It suits today the weak and base,
Whose minds are fixed on self and place;
To cringe before the rich man's frown,
And haul the sacred emblem down.

With heads uncovered swear we all,
To bear it onward till we fall;
Come dungeon dark or gallows grim,
This song shall be our parting hymn.

There's Something About A Soldier

There's something about a soldier,
Something about a soldier,
Something about a soldier that is fine, fine, fine.
He may be a great big general,
He may be a sergeant major,
May be a simple private of the line, line, line.
But there's something about his bearing,
Something in what he's wearing,
Something about his buttons all a-shine, shine, shine.
Oh, a military chest seems to suit the ladies best,
There's something about a soldier that is fine, fine, fine.

The Rose Of Tralee

The pale moon was rising above the green mountain,
The sun was declining beneath the blue sea,
When I strayed with my love to the pure crystal fountain
That stands in the beautiful vale of Tralee.
She was lovely and fair as the rose of the summer,
Yet 'twas not her beauty alone that won me.
Oh, no, 'twas the truth in her eyes ever dawning,
That made me love Mary, the rose of Tralee.

The Star-Spangled Banner

Oh say, can you see by the dawn's early light,
What so proudly we hailed at the twilight's last gleaming.
Whose broad stripes and bright stars through the perilous
                                                    flight,
O'er the ramparts we watched were so gallantly streaming?
And the rocket's red glare, the bombs bursting in air,
Gave proof through the night that our flag was still there.
Oh say, does that Star-Spangled Banner yet wave,
O'er the land of the free and the home of the brave?

On the shore dimly seen through the mists of the deep,
Where the foe's haughty host in dread silence reposes,
What is that which the breeze o'er the towering steep,
As it fitfully blows, half conceals, half discloses?
Now it catches the gleam of the morning's first beam;
Its full glory reflected now shines in the stream.
'Tis the Star-Spangled Banner, oh long may it wave
O'er the land of the free, and the home of the brave.

Oh, thus be it ever when free men shall stand
Between their loved homes and war's desolation;
Blest with victory and peace, may the Heaven-rescued land,
Praise the Power that hath made and preserved us a nation!
Then conquer we must, when our cause it is just,
And this is our motto, "In God is our Trust."
And the Star-Spangled Banner in triumph doth wave
O'er the land of the free, and the home of the brave.

The Tavern In The Town

There is a tavern in the town, in the town,
And there my true love sits him down, sits him down,
And drinks his wine 'mid laughter free,
And never, never thinks of me.

Chorus Fare thee well, for I must leave thee,
Do not let this parting grieve thee,
And remember that the best of friends must part,
must part,
Adieu, adieu, kind friends, adieu, adieu, adieu.
I can no longer stay with you, stay with you,
I'll hang my harp on a weeping willow tree,
And may the world go well with thee.

He left me for a damsel dark, damsel dark,
Each Friday night they used to spark, used to spark,
And now my love once true to me,
Takes that dark damsel on his knee.

Oh, dig my grave both wide and deep, wide and deep,
Put tombstones at my head and feet, head and feet,
And on my breast carve a turtle dove,
To signify I died of love.

The Washing On The Siegfried Line

We're going to hang out the washing on the Siegfried Line,
Have you any dirty washing, mother dear?
We're going to hang out the washing on the Siegfried Line,
'Cos the washing day is here.
Whether the weather may be wet or fine
We'll just rub along without a care.
We're going to hang out the washing on the Siegfried Line,
If the Siegfried Line's still there.

Tiptoe Through The Tulips

Tiptoe to the window, by the window,
That is where I'll be,
Come, tiptoe through the tulips with me;
Tiptoe from your pillow to the shadow
Of a willow tree,
And tiptoe through the tulips with me.
Knee deep in flowers we'll stray,
We'll keep the showers away;
And if I kiss you in the garden,
In the moonlight,
Will you pardon me,
Come tiptoe through the tulips with me.

Underneath The Arches

Underneath the arches I dream my dreams away,
Underneath the arches on cobblestones I lay,
Ev'ry night you'll find me, tired out and worn,
Happy when the daylight comes creeping,
Heralding the dawn.
Sleeping when it's raining, and sleeping when it's fine,
I hear the trains rattling by above,
Pavement is my pillow, no matter where I stray,
Underneath the arches I dream my dreams away.

Waltzing Matilda

Once a jolly swagman camped by a billabong
Under the shade of a coolibah tree,
And he sang as he watched and waited till his billy boiled,
"You'll come a-waltzing Matilda with me."

Chorus "Waltzing Matilda, waltzing Matilda,
You'll come a-waltzing Matilda with me."
And he sang as he watched and waited till his billy
boiled,
"You'll come a-waltzing Matilda with me."

Down came a jumbuck to drink at the billabong,
Up jumped a swagman and grabbed him with glee,
And he sang as he stowed that jumbuck in his tucker bag,
"You'll come a-waltzing Matilda with me."

We'll Keep A Welcome

We'll keep a welcome in the hillsides,
We'll keep a welcome in the glen,
This land you knew will still be singing
When you come home, sweet home, again;
There'll be a friendly light to guide you,
For your return we'll always pray;
We'll kiss away each hour of longing
When you come home again some day.

We'll keep a welcome in the hillsides,
We'll keep a welcome in the vales,
This land you knew will still be singing
When you come home again to Wales.
This land of song will keep a welcome,
And with a love that never fails,
We'll kiss away each hour of Hiraeth
When you come home again to Wales.
We'll kiss away each hour of Hiraeth
When you come home again to Wales.

When I'm Sixty Four

When I get older, losing my hair,
Many years from now,
Will you still be sending me a Valentine,
Birthday greetings, bottle of wine?
If I'd been out till quarter to three,
Would you lock the door?
Will you still need me, will you still feed me,
When I'm sixty-four?

I could be handy mending a fuse
When your lights have gone.
You can knit a sweater by the fireside,
Sunday mornings, go for a ride.
Doing the garden, digging the weeds;
Who could ask for more?
Will you still need me, will you still feed me,
When I'm sixty-four?

Send me a postcard, drop me a line,
Stating point of view.
Indicate precisely what you mean to say,
Yours sincerely, wasting away.
Give me your answer, fill in a form,
Mine for evermore.
Will you still need me, will you still feed me,
When I'm sixty-four?

When You're Smiling

When you're smiling, when you're smiling,
The whole world smiles with you;
When you're laughing, when you're laughing,
The sun comes shining through;
But when you're crying you bring on the rain,
So stop your sighing, be happy again;
Keep on smiling, 'cause when you're smiling,
The whole world smiles with you.

Yellow Submarine

In the town where I was born lived a man who sailed to sea.
And he told us of his life in the land of submarines.
So we sailed up to the sun till we found the sea of green.
And we lived beneath the waves in our yellow submarine.

Chorus We all live in a yellow submarine, yellow
submarine, yellow submarine.
We all live in a yellow submarine, yellow
submarine, yellow submarine.

And our friends are all on board, many more of them live
next door.
And the band begins to play.

As we live a life of ease, ev'ry one of us has all we need.
Sky of blue and sea of green in our yellow submarine.

Yesterday

Yesterday,
All my troubles seemed so far away,
Now it looks as though they're here to stay,
Oh, I believe in yesterday.
Suddenly,
I'm not half the man I used to be,
There's a shadow hanging over me.
Oh, yesterday came suddenly.

Why she had to go I don't know,
She wouldn't say.
I said something wrong,
Now I long for yesterday.

Yesterday,
Love was such an easy game to play,
Now I need a place to hide away.
Oh, I believe in yesterday.

You Are My Sunshine

The other night, dear,
As I lay dreaming,
I dreamt that you were by my side.
Came disillusion
When I awoke, dear,
You were gone and then I cried:

Chorus You are my sunshine,
My only sunshine,
You make me happy
When skies are grey.
You'll never know, dear,
How much I love you;
Please don't take my sunshine away.

I'll always love you
And make you happy,
If you will only do the same.
But if you leave me,
How it will grieve me;
Nevermore I'll breathe your name.

You Made Me Love You

You made me love you,
I didn't want to do it, I didn't want to do it.
You made me want you,
And all the time you knew it, I guess you always knew it.
You made me happy sometimes, you made me glad,
But there were times, dear, you made me feel so bad.
You made me sigh for,
I didn't want to tell you, I didn't want to tell you,
I want some love, that's true,
Yes I do, 'deed I do, you know I do.
Give me, give me what I cry for,
You know you've got the brand of kisses that I'd die for,
You know you made me love you.

Yours

Yours till the stars lose their glory,
Yours till the birds fail to sing,
Yours to the end of life's story,
This pledge to you, dear, I bring.
Yours in the grey of December
Here or on far distant shores;
I've never loved anyone the way I love you,
How could I?
When I was born to be just yours?

List of Songs